Little Caterpillar is Cold

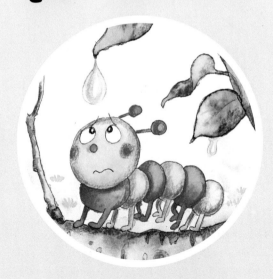

by Anne Giulieri

illustrated by Mélanie Florian

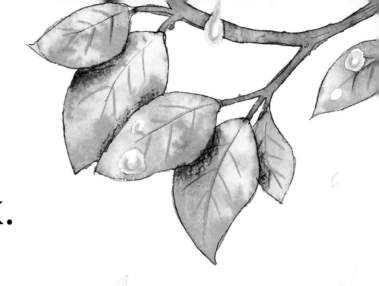

I am cold
on the stick.

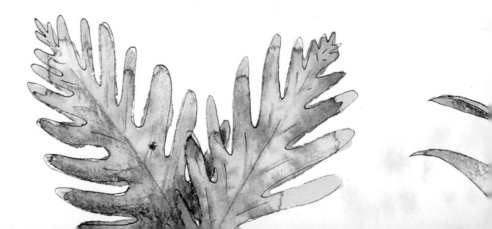

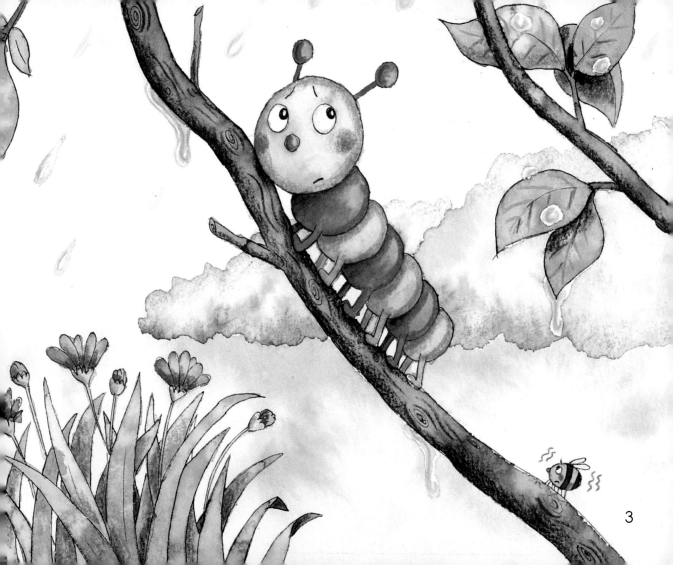

I am cold
on the rock.

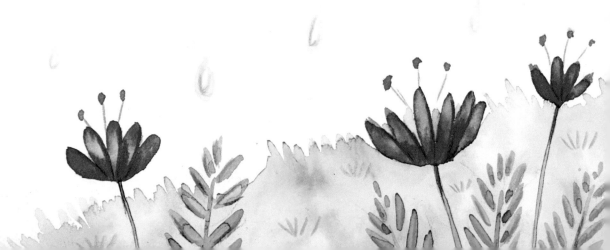

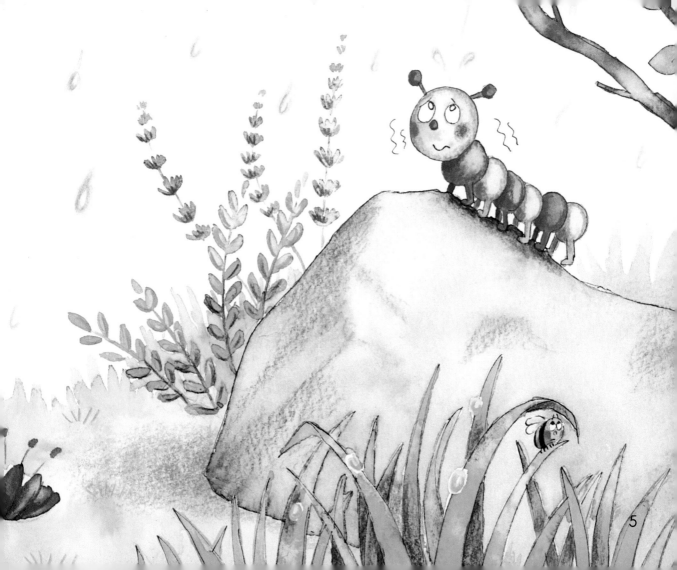

I am cold
on the grass.

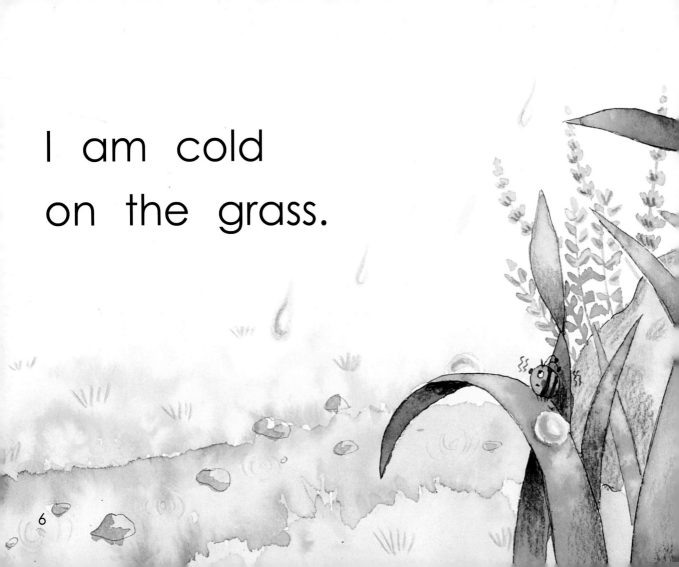

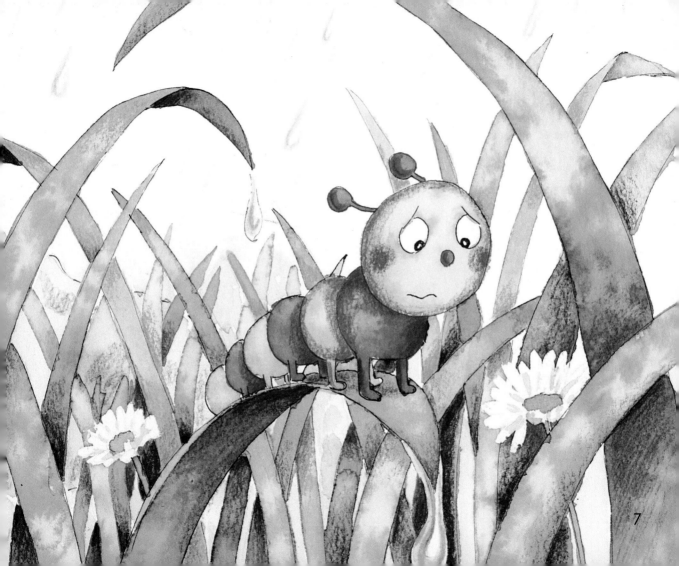

I am cold
on the path.

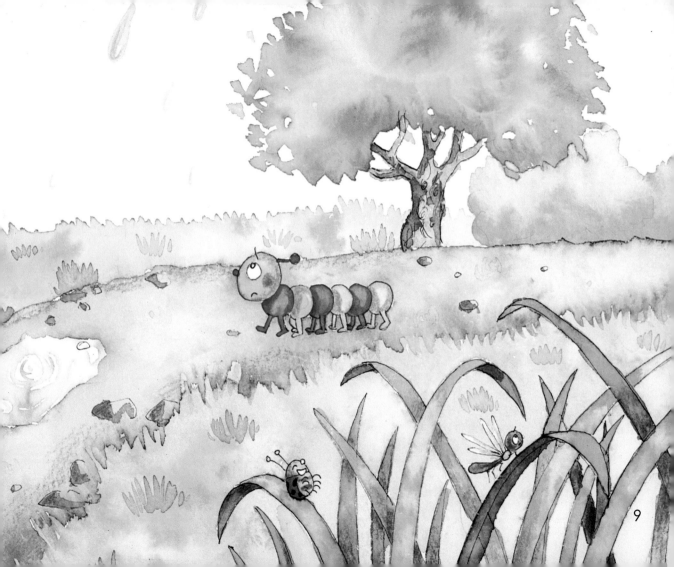

I am cold
on the flower.

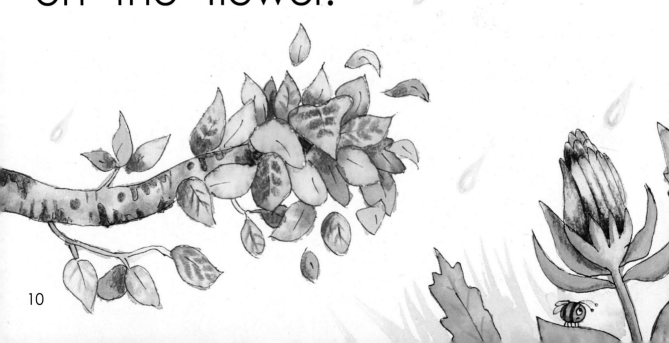

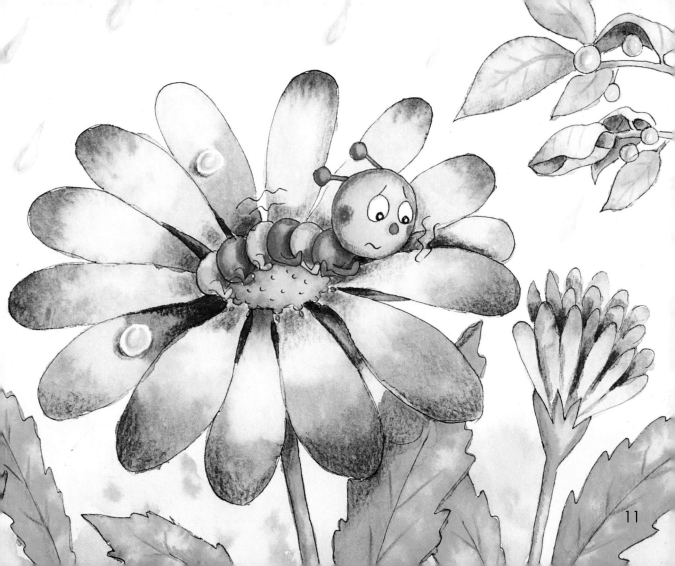

I am cold
on the tree.

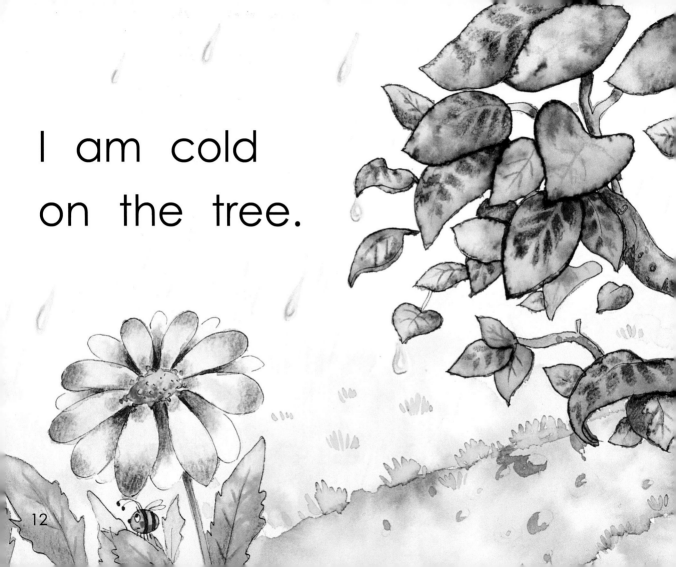

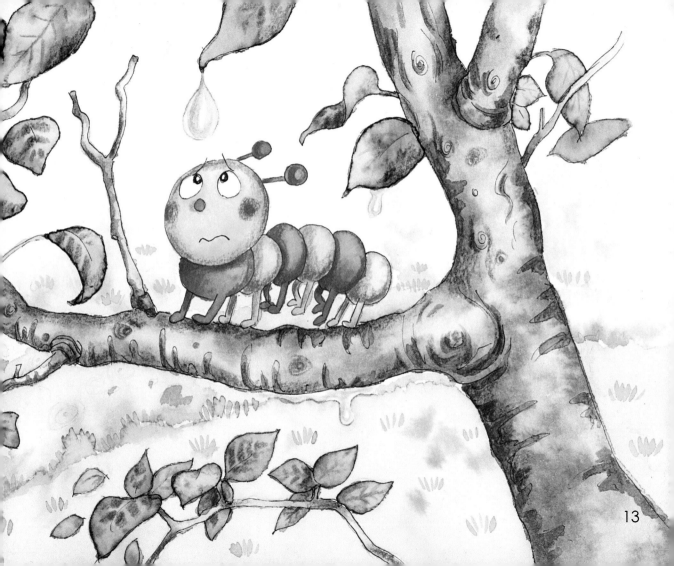

13

Look!
I am warm
on the leaf.

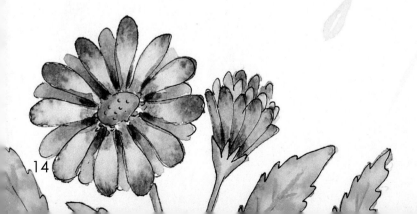

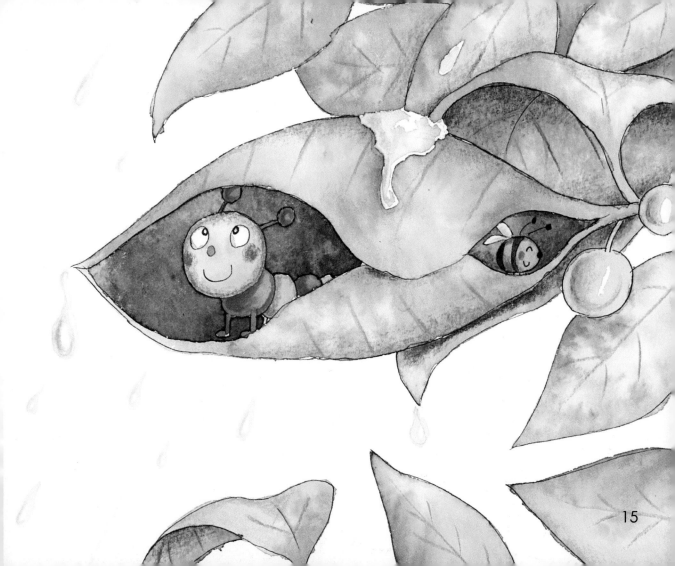

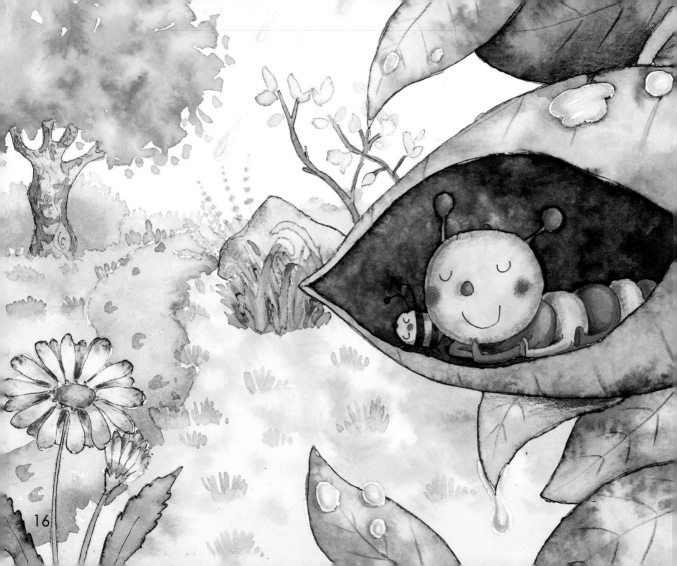